BELAIR
ACTIVE SCIENCE 5

Patricia Young

Contents

Belair
Publications

First published in 2000 by Belair Publications.
Apex Business Centre, Boscombe Road, Dunstable, LU5 4RL.
Email: belair@belair-publications.co.uk

Editor: Hayley Willer
Layout artist: Suzanne Ward
Illustrations: Virginia Gray (Graham-Cameron Illustration)
Cover design: Martin Cross

British Library Cataloguing in Publication Data. A catalogue record for this publication is available from the British Library.

ISBN 1 84191 074-0

Introduction

Active Science is a series of six books designed to be used with children aged five to eleven. The series provides teachers' notes and worksheets matched to the QCA Scheme of Work for Science.

The activities included in the book are varied and challenging and encourage the children to think scientifically. The emphasis is on providing the children with first-hand experience of scientific practical work and investigation.

Active Science 5 can be used alongside the QCA Scheme as the basis of a year's work or it can be used to supplement existing schemes of work already in place in school.

The book is divided into eleven chapters. Each chapter consists of a teachers' page and three photocopiable activity sheets.

What is on the teachers' page?

- **Background** – This provides the necessary background knowledge for teachers to deliver the topic. This is not information that the children are required to know necessarily, but information to aid the teacher.

- **Activity pages** – This section contains:
  - the main learning objectives in terms of knowledge, understanding and skills, for each activity, to help teachers with planning and assessment
  - ideas for further activities
  - guidance points for discussion
  - safety warnings.

- **Oral work** – This section provides opportunities for:
  - discussion
  - questioning that encourages the children to think about the scientific process
  - oral presentations
  - interviewing
  - inviting guest speakers into the classroom
  - role-play.

- **Written work** – This section provides ideas for written work, including:
  - comparing and contrasting
  - producing leaflets and guides on certain scientific issues
  - planning investigations
  - writing conclusions and explanations
  - full scientific report writing.

- **ICT** – A range of opportunities for the use of ICT in the Science Curriculum is provided, including:
  - researching information using CD-ROM and the Internet
  - using ICT programs to produce scientific information in the form of text and graphics
  - using computer databases
  - using data-handling packages to present results of experiments
  - using audiotapes and videotapes to record work.

What about the activity pages?

The photocopiable worksheets contain a variety of activities that provide opportunities for the children to do the following.

- **Plan** – This includes:
  - making predictions
  - considering what evidence is to be collected
  - planning investigations and fair tests.

- **Obtain and present evidence** – This includes:
  - making careful observations and measurements
  - using simple apparatus
  - choosing methods of recording
  - recording results systematically.

- **Consider evidence and evaluate** – This includes:
  - making comparisons
  - using results to draw conclusions
  - explaining in terms of scientific knowledge and understanding
  - considering whether a test is fair or not
  - deciding how an investigation could be improved.

Background

Cells in the body convert sugar and oxygen into water and carbon dioxide and produce energy in the process. If the body requires more energy then the blood flows faster to the cells and more oxygen will be available to burn the sugars. During exercise the breathing rate and the heart rate increase so that more blood containing more oxygen is transported to the cells. The waste products of carbon dioxide and water are taken away from the cells and expelled via the lungs.

Regular exercise increases the number of capillaries in the lungs so that more oxygen can be absorbed. The alveoli or air sacs in the lungs become larger and the muscles associated with breathing become larger and stronger. All these changes help to make the respiratory system work more efficiently.

Tobacco contains nicotine, which is addictive. It also contains tar that clogs up tiny hairs called cilia in our lungs. The hairs help to keep the lungs clean and the alveoli healthy. Carbon monoxide is also found in tobacco smoke. It is a poison that causes heart disease. Smoking is the most common cause of cancer in the UK. About 100 000 people a year die in the UK due to tobacco smoking. Inhaling other people's smoke (passive smoking) is also harmful.

Activity pages

Pulse and Breathing Rates

Learning objectives
- To record pulse and breathing rates.
- To communicate results in graphical form.
- To interpret results.

Show the children how to take the pulse rate. Use fingers (not thumbs) on the wrist in line with the children's thumb.

Discuss how the experiment could be made better, for example by repeating the readings for each person and taking the pulse and breathing rates at 15-second intervals.

Ask the children to time how long it takes for the pulse and breathing rates to return to normal. Is there a link between the fitness of the children and the time it takes for their pulse rate to return to normal? Explain the health benefits of regular exercise.

Heart and Circulation

Learning objectives
- To understand that the muscles in the walls of the heart pump blood around the body.
- To understand that there are vessels that carry blood around the body.

Before completing the table, the children could first make notes from the passage using keywords or a spidergram.

Smoking and Health

Learning objectives
- To understand that smoking affects health and that the effects can be harmful.

The following sentences on the activity sheet are *incorrect*: d, g, k, n.

Oral work

Encourage the children to describe how the circulatory and respiratory systems work together to help maintain a healthy body. If the body is to stay healthy, it must be well treated. This means having regular exercise and not taking harmful materials into the body.

Written work

Ask the children to design a leaflet explaining to other children why it is important that they exercise regularly.

ICT

Ask the children to carry out a survey by collecting ages and pulse rates of children from Reception to Year 6 and of staff at the school. The data from all the children and staff could be put into a spreadsheet and displayed graphically. Ask questions such as 'Does pulse rate change with age?' or 'What is the most common pulse rate?'. Other factors such as weight and gender might be considered.

Pulse and Breathing Rates

You will need
- Stopwatch
- Skipping rope

 **Key Idea**   Exercise affects our breathing and pulse rates.

● Working in pairs, take it in turns to be the pulse rate and breathing rate recorder and to be the subject having your pulse rate and breathing rate recorded.

1. Measure the pulse rate and breathing rate of your partner while he or she is sitting. Count for 15 seconds and multiply the number by four to calculate the rate per minute. Record the results in the table. Take the pulse rate and breathing rate immediately after your partner has done the activities in the table.

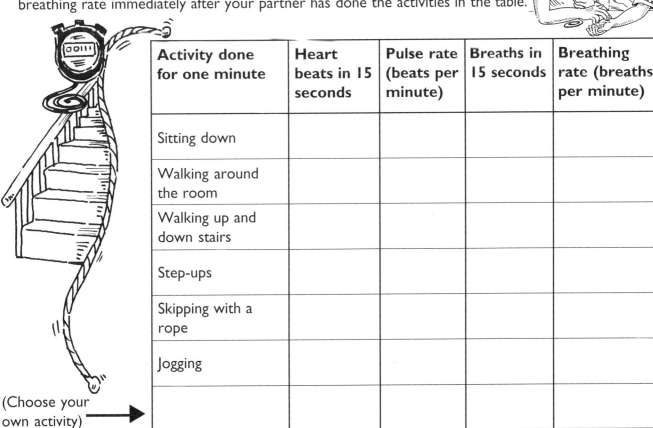

Activity done for one minute	Heart beats in 15 seconds	Pulse rate (beats per minute)	Breaths in 15 seconds	Breathing rate (breaths per minute)
Sitting down				
Walking around the room				
Walking up and down stairs				
Step-ups				
Skipping with a rope				
Jogging				
(Choose your own activity)				

2. Draw a bar chart of pulse rate against activity for yourself.

3. a. Now draw a bar chart of breathing rate against activity for yourself.
   b. What do you notice from the bar charts?

4. How did the pulse rates change compared to the breathing rates for the different activities?

5. a. Make a list of sitting pulse rates for every child in the class. Order this list from slowest to fastest.
   b. How does your sitting pulse rate compare with others' sitting pulse rates? What is the most common pulse rate? What is the fastest and what is the slowest rate?

 **NOW**   What do you think would happen to your pulse rate and breathing rate if you did the activities for longer? Choose one activity to see if your prediction is correct.

Heart and Circulation

You will need

– Calculator

Key Idea The heart is part of the circulatory system. It pumps blood around the body. Blood carries materials to and from all parts of the body.

1. Read this passage.

Cells in our body need to be given the right materials if they are to work properly.
All the substances are taken to the cells by our blood. Every cell has to be very near to a blood supply.

The circulatory system makes sure that every cell has a supply of blood. The circulatory system is made up of the heart and blood vessels. Your heart is about the size of your fist and weighs about 250g. It beats about 70 times a minute and pumps blood around your body. Every time it pumps, it forces about 100ml of blood away from the heart. This blood is carried in vessels around the body. The blood goes to the lungs, brain and all the muscles in the body.

2. Complete the table. Show your working out.

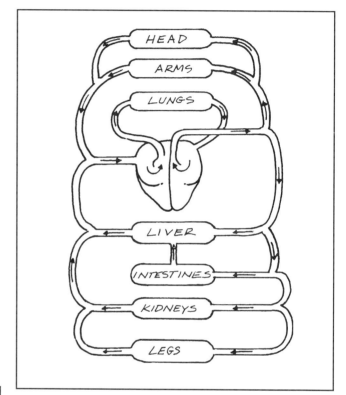

The circulatory system.

Number of heart beats for an average person:	
In a minute	
In an hour	
In 24 hours	
In a week	
In a year	
In 10 years	
Volume of blood forced away from the heart in one squeeze	
Volume of blood forced away from the heart in ten years	

Smoking and Health

Key Idea — Smoking affects the way the body works. The effects can be harmful.

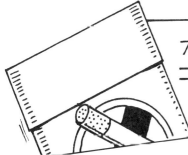

You will need

– Calculator

1. Read the following sentences. Put a tick beside those that you think are correct.

TOBACCO SERIOUSLY DAMAGES HEALTH!

a. Over 90% of people who die of lung cancer or heart disease are smokers.

b. People who smoke over 20 cigarettes a day may become disabled by ill health.

c. Babies of mothers who smoke are often smaller than babies of mothers who do not smoke.

d. Children who smoke will probably not smoke when they get older.

e. The younger a child starts to smoke the more likely he/she is to be a life-long smoker.

f. Smoking stains teeth and fingers yellow.

g. It is legal to sell cigarettes to anybody under 16 years old.

h. Smokers' breath, hair and clothes smell of stale tobacco.

i. People who smoke are more likely to have coughs and colds.

j. Cigarettes contain a habit-forming drug called nicotine.

k. Breathing in another person's cigarette smoke is not harmful.

l. People's smoking can harm other people around them.

m. Cigarette packets in Britain must carry a government health warning.

n. There is no real proof that smoking can kill.

PROTECT CHILDREN. DON'T MAKE THEM BREATHE YOUR SMOKE!

2. Make an anti-smoking poster aimed at children in your school.

NOW — Find out how much a packet of 20 cigarettes costs. How much would a smoker spend if they smoked a packet every day of the year?

Background

Foods can be classified into different groups: those that are needed for growth and repair, those that are needed for energy, and those that are needed to keep the body working normally by preventing deficiency diseases. Proteins belong to the first set of foods, and carbohydrates and fats belong to the second. Minerals and vitamins belong to the third set. Carbohydrates are made up of starch and sugars. Dietary fibre or roughage is not digested by the body but helps to keep it healthy. The other essential ingredient in the diet is water. A balanced diet contains food from each food group.

The body uses food to release energy during respiration. The energy enables the organs to work continuously, the tissues to be repaired, the muscles to work and the body's temperature to be maintained at 37°C. The amount of energy needed by the body depends on the activity being carried out. Males and females use different amounts of energy. The amount of energy is usually measured in kilojoules. A kilojoule is the amount of energy you use when you lift a 1kg mass 1m off the floor. An 11-year-old boy will typically use 10 000 kJ per day whereas an 11-year-old girl will use 9 200kJ.

Activity pages

Testing for Fats
Learning objectives
- To identify that some foods contain fat.
- To identify by investigation those foods that contain fat.

Discuss the fact that it is important not to have too high an intake of fat into the diet. Fatty foods contain more energy than other foods. If this energy is not used by the body it is stored as fat under the skin and around the organs. It can also be stored in the arteries, which could eventually clog them up, causing the heart to work harder to pump blood around the body. This causes people to become unhealthy and may lead to illness and shorter life. People who are trying to lose weight sometimes have a low-fat diet.

However, because fat gives us energy, children in particular need fat in order to grow. Fat-free diets are therefore not appropriate for children.

Food Labels
Learning objectives
- To identify that foods contain a variety of nutrients.
- To interpret food labels.

The children should bring in food labels from, for example, baked beans, noodles, fizzy drinks, pasta sauces, biscuits, pâté, etc. Food labels can give us important information about the food we eat and interpreting them is a useful skill. Remind the children that to stay healthy we need to consume foods from each food group.

Children will find the most common ingredients to be either salt, sugar or water. Salt and sugar are used to help to preserve the food. Sugar helps improve the flavour. Water is often the most common ingredient in sauces.

A Balanced Diet
Learning objectives
- To understand that energy in food is used to provide our body with energy.
- To understand that we need a varied diet.
- To identify that the amount of food needed by our body depends on what we are doing.
- To develop a balanced menu.

Oral work

Discuss the importance of a healthy diet and the consequences of too much fat (obesity and heart disease) and too much sugar (tooth decay). Encourage children to compare their own diet with a balanced diet.

What nutrients, if any, do the children feel that they do not get enough of?

Written work

Ask the children to develop a class newspaper that focuses on healthy eating. This could contain suggestions for healthy meals and include low-fat or low-sugar recipes that they have tried. It might include an 'agony aunt' page so that the children can offer advice to others.

ICT

Spreadsheets can be used to display the proportion of nutrients in different foodstuffs.

Desktop publishing can be used for the creation of a class newspaper.

CD-ROMs and the Internet could be used for research.

Changing Shadows

Hugo Wilmot

The length of a shadow depends on different factors including the distance of the light from the object, the distance of the surface on which the shadow is cast from the object and the angle at which the light meets the object.

You will need
- Darkened room
- Torch
- Pencil
- Plasticine to secure pencil

1. Working in a darkened room, shine the torch on to the pencil, keeping the torch about 30cm from the pencil, and observe where the shadow is. Make the length of the shadow as short as possible.

2. Explain why you think the shadow is so short. Draw a diagram in the box below to help you to explain.

I think its short because the Girl is shining it down and because its close to the wall.

3. Make the length of the shadow as long as possible.

4. Explain why you think the shadow is so long. Draw a diagram in the box below to help you to explain.

I think because the pencils close to the torch

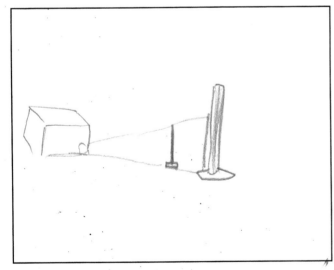

5. If a metre stick was placed upright and outside on a sunny day, how can the results of the activity you have just done relate to the length of the stick's shadow changing throughout the day?

I don't know

Testing for Fats

 **Key Idea**

Fats provide the body with energy. Foods can be tested to see if they contain fats.

You will need
- Small pieces of bread, margarine, potato, apple, chocolate, cheese, crisp, sugar, cooked pasta
- Greaseproof paper

1. Rub a small piece of food on to the greaseproof paper. Hold the paper up to the light. If there is a shiny mark on the paper that allows more light to pass through, then the food contains fat.

2. Test all the foods in this way to find out which contain fat. Record your results in the table below.

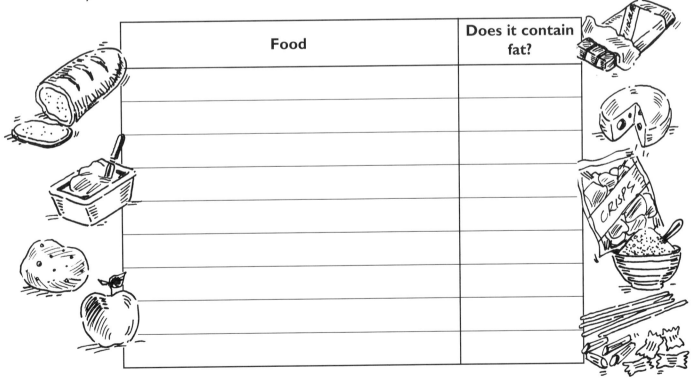

Food	Does it contain fat?

 **NOW** Find out what happens to people who eat too much fat.

Food Labels

Key Idea

Processed food usually contains several ingredients. Different foods contain different amounts of protein, carbohydrate and fat and supply different amounts of energy.

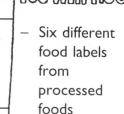
1. a. Look at your six different food labels. Make a table that shows the name of the food in one column and all the ingredients in the next.
   b. Which food contains the highest number of ingredients?

2. What do you think might happen to the food if some of the ingredients were left out?

3. a. Which ingredient is most commonly used?
   b. Why do you think that this ingredient is used in foods?

4. How many grams of protein, carbohydrate, fat and fibre are there in 100g of each food? Record your results in a table like the one below. Write the amount to the nearest gram.

Food	Grams of protein	Grams of carbohydrate	Grams of fat	Grams of fibre
Chocolate biscuit	6	60	24	1
Margarine	1	1	70	0

5. Why do you think that the numbers do not add up to 100? The labels may give you some more information.

6. a. Draw a bar chart, like the one below, to show the amount of protein, carbohydrate, fat and fibre in 100g of each food.
   b. Which food has the most protein?
   c. Which food has the most carbohydrate?
   d. Which food has the most fat?
   e. Which food has the most fibre?

7. Eating too much fat can cause disease. Why could it be unhealthy to eat fried bread for breakfast, crisps for lunch and chips for tea?

8. What foods would you recommend to weight lifters trying to develop their muscles?

9. What foods would you take on a hike?

NUMBER OF GRAMS

PROTEIN
CARBOHYDRATE
FAT
FIBRE

CHOCOLATE BISCUIT   MARGARINE

NOW   Use reference books to find out which vitamins the body needs and why.

A Balanced Diet

 **Key Idea**

The energy in food is used to provide our body with energy. The amount of food needed by our body depends on what we are doing. To stay healthy we need an adequate and varied diet.

1. Below is a table of some activities you might do during a day at the weekend. Write in the number of hours that you spent doing each of the activities during a 24-hour period.

2. For each activity, calculate how much energy your body used.

3. Calculate how much energy your body used over the whole day.

Activity	Energy used in an hour in kilojoules	Number of hours spent on the activity	Amount of energy used in kilojoules
Sleeping	200		
Sitting	300		
Light activity, for example tidying your bedroom, playing snooker	600		
Moderate activity, for example ironing, washing the car	800		
Walking	1000		
Cycling	1600		
Swimming	1800		
Energetic sport, for example football	2200		
Total			

4. **a.** An average bar of chocolate contains about 800kJ. If you ate nothing but chocolate during the day, how many chocolate bars would your body need?

   b. Would it be a good idea to eat nothing but chocolate? Why?

 **NOW**

Use information from food labels to make a balanced menu for yourself for the day. Make sure that the foods you choose contain enough kilojoules for your energy needs and also each of the nutrients: protein, carbohydrate, fat, vitamins, minerals and fibre so that you receive a balanced diet.

Life Cycles of Plants

The life cycle of flowering plants includes the processes of pollination, fertilisation, seed dispersal and germination.

Pollination is usually carried out by wind or by insects. Wind-pollinated flowers are usually small, green or dull coloured and hang downwards so that the pollen can be shaken away easily. Insect-pollinated flowers are usually larger, brightly coloured and have nectar.

Seeds are the result of successful fertilisation and they are dispersed in a variety of ways. Light seeds can be dispersed by the wind. They may have wings to help them travel further, for example sycamore. Coconuts are sometimes carried by water. They contain a lot of air, which helps them to float. Other seeds may contain hooks so that they can be attached to an animal's fur, for example burdock. Other animals may bury nuts as a food supply, for example squirrels burying acorns or beechnuts.

The process of a seed producing a new plant is called germination. At the centre of the seed is the embryo, which is the part that is capable of growing. Surrounding this is the endosperm. This supplies the seed with food. The conditions needed for germination are:
- water; this causes the seed to swell and burst open
- oxygen; seeds need to respire so that they have the energy for germination
- suitable temperature; this varies with the plant.

Light is not necessary for most seeds to germinate. However, once they have germinated and have their first leaves they will need light in order to photosynthesise their own food.

Activity pages

Flowering Plants
Learning objectives
- To be able to identify the reproductive organs of flowering plants.
- To know the processes involved in sexual reproduction in plants.

You could use this sheet as part of a class activity – enlarge the picture of the flower and ask the children to label it. Pin the picture to the wall and ask the children to write about the life cycle of a flowering plant using the picture as a guide.

Identifying Fruits and Seeds
Learning objectives
- To understand that seeds can be dispersed in a variety of ways.
- To identify fruits and seeds using a branching key.

You may need to adapt this activity, depending on the time of year and what seeds you have available for the children to look at.

Safety – Demonstrate the holly berries yourself as they are poisonous.

Germinating Pea Seeds
Learning objectives
- To consider conditions that might affect germination.
- To understand that several seeds should be used in each set of conditions in order to get reliable evidence.
- To make careful observations and comparisons.

Discuss how we should make the experiment fair, i.e. the seeds should be sown in the same amount of soil and the pots should be placed in the same position in the classroom.

Pea seeds will take up water during soaking. The children should find that the unsoaked seeds take longer to germinate because they need to take in water before their seed coat splits open.

Oral work

Encourage the children to look at different types of plants and discuss whether they reproduce by flower production. Ensure that the children use the correct vocabulary when discussing reproduction.

Discuss the need for a plant to produce many seeds so that it ensures that at least some of its seeds will germinate and so that the species can colonise other places. Talk about how plants 'know' when to germinate (when the temperature is warm enough and the soil moist).

Written work

Ask the children to describe, in words or pictures, the life cycle of a flowering plant.

The children could research plants that are useful to us (e.g. wheat, potato).

ICT

Ask children to research and produce a database of wild flowers in the local area.

Flowering Plants

Key Idea

The life cycle of flowering plants includes the processes of pollination, fertilisation and seed development.

● The flower contains the plant's reproductive organs. It is made up of different parts. Read the information below and then draw arrows from each box to the correct part of the flower.

Pollen is very small. It needs to travel to the stigma of another plant. This process is called pollination. Sometimes the wind helps the pollen to travel or sometimes insects take the pollen to another plant.

The **stamens** are the male part of the flower. They surround the carpel, and look a bit like pins. They are made up of the anther and the filament.

The **carpel** is the female part of the flower. It is made up of two parts – the stigma and the style.

The **anther** is at the top of the stamen. It contains the pollen.

The **stigma** is in the middle of the ring of stamens, forming the top of the carpel. It is sticky in order to catch the pollen.

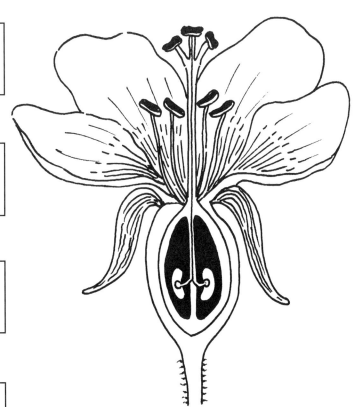

The **filament** is the long tube that forms part of the stamen.

The **style** is the stalk that supports the stigma. The pollen moves down the style.

The **petals** are often brightly coloured to attract insects.

The **ovary** is at the bottom of the style. This is where the pollen and the egg in the ovary join together. This process is called fertilisation. The fertilised egg grows into a seed. The ovary turns into a fruit.

The **sepals** are green and leaf-like and protect the bud before opening.

NOW

Think of a plant that is common in your area. Look in books to find out what the flower and seed look like. Find out how the flowers are pollinated and how the seeds are dispersed.

Draw a diagram to show the life cycle of the flowering plant you have researched.

Identifying Fruits and Seeds

Key Idea — Plants have fruits to feed the growing seeds inside and to help disperse the seeds.

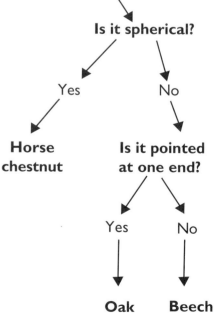

You will need
- Fruits from trees

1. Use the tree diagram to identify which trees the following fruits come from. Write the correct name under each.

_____   _____   _____

_____   _____   _____

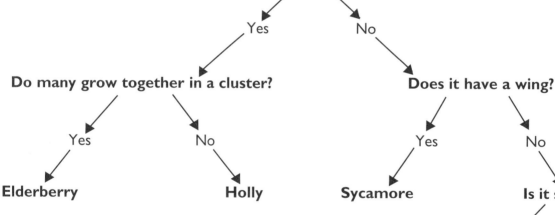

Can you squash the fruit between your fingers?

Yes → **Do many grow together in a cluster?**

No → **Does it have a wing?**

Do many grow together in a cluster?
- Yes → **Elderberry**
- No → **Holly**

Does it have a wing?
- Yes → **Sycamore**
- No → **Is it spherical?**

Is it spherical?
- Yes → **Horse chestnut**
- No → **Is it pointed at one end?**

Is it pointed at one end?
- Yes → **Oak**
- No → **Beech**

• Seeds need to move away from the parent plant so that they can obtain enough water and light to grow. The fruits help the seeds to be dispersed. Each type of seed is dispersed in one main way. The two most common ways in which seeds are dispersed are by wind or animals. Animals may eat berries and excrete the seed. Sometimes the fruit gets stuck to an animal's body and is dropped away from the plant. Sometimes the animals bury them.

2. How are the seeds of the above trees dispersed? If animals are involved, which animals might they be?
3. List three other seeds that are dispersed by the wind.
4. How are the fruits adapted so that the seeds are carried by the wind?
5. List three other seeds that are dispersed by animals. How are the fruits adapted so that the seeds can be dispersed?

Germinating Pea Seeds

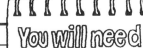

You will need

- 100g pea seeds
- Beaker
- Kitchen towel
- Weighing scales
- Ten soaked pea seeds
- Ten unsoaked pea seeds
- Two transparent containers with compost

 **Key Idea**   Seeds need moisture to germinate.

● Before sowing pea seeds, gardeners often soak them in water overnight. This activity will help you to find out what happens to the seeds and explain why gardeners soak them.

1. Place 100g of pea seeds in a beaker and cover with water.
   After one hour, drain off the water.
   Dry the peas with a kitchen towel and find their mass (weight).
   Put your results in a table like the one below.
   Replace them in the beaker and cover with water.
   After each hour repeat the draining, weighing and soaking.
   Repeat for as many hours as you have available.
   Leave the peas soaking overnight and weigh the next morning.

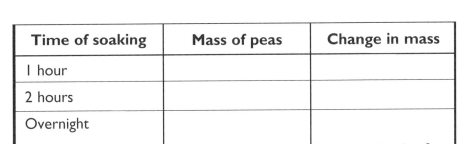

Time of soaking	Mass of peas	Change in mass
1 hour		
2 hours		
Overnight		

2. Plot a graph of mass of peas against time of soaking as shown opposite.

3. During which time did the seeds take in most water?

4. Sow the ten soaked pea seeds and the ten unsoaked pea seeds in the transparent containers. Label each pot either 'soaked' or 'unsoaked'. Water the peas daily.

5. Observe the pots each day and record how many seedlings are showing through.

Mass of peas

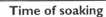

Time of soaking

Day	Number of soaked seedlings	Number of unsoaked seedlings
1		
2		
3		
4		

 **NOW**   Explain why one set of seeds germinated faster than the other set.

Life Cycles of Animals

Background

The life cycle of an animal is the progression from its formation to its death. Some of the changes that take place are drastic, for example metamorphosis from a caterpillar to a butterfly. Other changes take place more slowly, for example growth of a human baby into an adult.

Growth takes place by cells enlarging and dividing. In a human not all parts of the body grow at the same rate. In babies the head is the fastest growing part of the body, whilst legs and arms grow more slowly at first but grow more quickly during adolescence. When no more cells are added to the body, it stops growing. This is usually around the age of 18. The body continues to make cells to repair any damaged cells. Hormones help to activate the body to grow during certain parts of the life cycle. Thyroxin is a hormone that helps children to grow.

Insects have a hard skin or cuticle that cannot stretch as they grow. Instead, the cuticle is cast off or moulted.

The insect forms a liquid under the cuticle that dissolves most of the shell. It blows itself up with air, which splits the remaining cuticle so that the insect can finish removing it. The softer cuticle underneath gradually hardens and the process repeats itself.

Puberty in humans is the time when the testes begin to make sperm and the ovaries start to produce eggs. Other changes that take place in the male's body during puberty are a lowering of the voice and growth of hair on the legs, chest and face. A female's breasts begin to develop, she begins to menstruate and grows more body hair.

The gestation period in most mammals is related to the size of the animal at birth, i.e. the larger the mammal, the longer the gestation period. However, there is variation within species.

Activity pages

Growing Up
Learning objectives
- To know that human young are dependent upon adults for a relatively long time.
- To compare and contrast characteristics of toddlers and themselves.

Ask the children to think about the changes that may occur to them in the next five years – maybe by comparing themselves with older siblings or cousins. They could draw a picture of how they think they might look in the future.

Life Cycles of Invertebrates
Learning objectives
- To identify that the life cycles of various animals are different.
- To be able to contrast a human's life cycle with an invertebrate's.

Gestation Periods
Learning objectives
- To know that different mammals have different gestation periods.
- To observe a pattern between animal size and gestation period.

Oral work

Ask the children about how the care that a human baby needs differs from that of other animals. Encourage them to discuss the differences between an adolescent and an adult. Though adolescents are physically able to reproduce they may not be emotionally able to care for a baby.

Written work

Ask the children to research the life cycles of other animals. They could produce a class fact sheet about unusual life cycles of animals.

ICT

Ask children to scan a recent photograph of themselves. They can then edit the picture to change their features so that they look older. They could make themselves look: 20 years old, 40 years old, 60 years old, 80 years old.

Ask the children to use CD-ROM to research other animals.

Growing Up

You will need
- Photograph taken when you were about two years old
- Recent photograph

Key Idea Human young are dependent on others for a relatively long time.

1. Look at the two photographs. In what ways have you changed since the first one was taken?

2. In the table below make a list of ten things you can do now that you could not do when you were first born (some are already done for you). Complete the table. You will need to ask other people the answers to some of the questions.

Activity	How old was I when I learned it?	How did I learn?	Who helped me?
Walk			
Ride a bike			
Talk in sentences			

3. Draw a time line to show when you learned to do the activities.

4. **a.** Make a list of five important things that you still need to learn.
   b. Add two of these things to the time line to show when you think you will be able to do them.

5. Make a list of four ways your body will change during adolescence.

 **NOW** What are the differences between an adolescent and an adult?

Life Cycles of Invertebrates

 **Key Idea**

Adults have young that grow into adults. Different animals have different life cycles.

1. Read about the life cycles of these four animals.

The ladybird

Ladybirds wake up from hibernation in early Spring and mate in Spring and Summer. About two days after mating, a female ladybird lays about 125 eggs on the underside of different leaves. The eggs hatch out as larvae within a week. As soon as they hatch out, they eat the remains of their shell. They also eat greenfly and other ladybird larvae. The ladybird eats so much that its skin splits. There is another skin underneath. After three weeks of eating and moulting, the ladybird larva changes into a pupa. The pupa has a tough skin. Inside the skin, the ladybird changes into a yellow spotless adult. After two weeks it hatches, turns red and grows spots. The old ladybirds die before winter. The new ladybirds find somewhere to hibernate until next Spring.

The earthworm

Earthworms begin to mate in early Summer. They have both male and female sex organs so can mate with any other earthworm. The worms lie side by side and swap sperm. After two or three days, the eggs from each worm are ready to be laid. The worm makes a thick ring of slime around its saddle. The saddle is the thicker part of the worm's body. The worm lays its eggs in the ring and then adds the sperm. It wriggles away from the ring of slime, which turns hard and forms a shell-like cocoon. Inside the cocoon there are many growing eggs. Usually only one egg from each cocoon survives. The egg hatches between one and five months later. It looks like a smaller version of an adult earthworm. After one year they have grown longer and produced a saddle. They are now ready to mate.

The woodlouse

Male and female woodlice mate in early Summer. The female then moults and grows a new skin that has a pouch. She lays about 200 eggs in the pouch. The eggs hatch in the pouch after 25 days. The baby woodlice leave the pouch after two days. They are white and have only six pairs of legs. (Adult woodlice have seven pairs of legs.) As the woodlouse grows, it moults and forms an extra set of legs. As Winter approaches, it burrows down into the earth to keep warm. After two years the woodlouse may be ready to mate. It may live for up to four years.

The garden spider

Garden spiders mate at the end of Summer. The male spins a silk cushion and squirts sperm on it. He then sucks this up and searches for a mate. When he has found her he puts the sperm in her sperm store, which is located on the underside of her abdomen. He has to do this very quickly so that he is not killed by the female. Even if he is not killed during mating, he will die a few days later anyway. The female then spins a silk cushion and lays about 200 eggs on it. The eggs are covered by silk. This is called a cocoon. The female soon dies. The eggs remain in the cocoon until Spring when the spiders begin to hatch. They eat their egg cases and sometimes the weaker spiderlings in the cocoon. After a week, each spiderling leaves the cocoon by spinning a thread. This catches the wind and carries the spiderling to a new home. As it grows during the rest of the Summer, it moults. By early Winter the spider has found a place to hibernate until the following Spring.

2. Choose one of the animals. Draw a diagram to show its life cycle.

 **NOW**

How is a human's life cycle different from the animal's that you have chosen?

Gestation Periods

You will need

– Calculator

Key Idea Different animals have different gestation periods.

- Mammals give birth to live young. After fertilisation, the animal grows inside its mother. Different animals need different times to develop before they are ready to be born. This time is called the gestation period. Here are some animals and their approximate gestation periods.

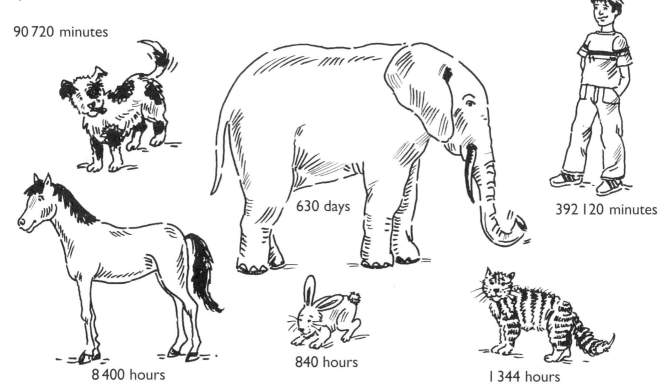

90 720 minutes

630 days

392 120 minutes

8 400 hours

840 hours

1 344 hours

1. List the animals from the smallest to the largest.
Use a calculator to find their gestation period in weeks.

Animal	Gestation period	Gestation period in weeks

2. What pattern is there between animal size and gestation period? Why?

 **NOW** Find the gestation period of other animals and see if they fit the pattern.

Air is a mixture of different gases. 78% of the air is made up of nitrogen and 21% of the air is oxygen. The amount of carbon dioxide is only about 0.03%. There is also water vapour, the amount of which changes as the weather changes. The amount of water vapour in the air ranges from 0% to 4%. There are some other gases that are useful to us but come in very small quantities. A group of these are called noble gases. Argon, helium, krypton, neon and xenon are noble gases. Air also contains pollutants, for example nitrous oxides, sulphur oxides and carbon monoxide. These come from industry, transport, homes and volcanoes.

Oxygen could be described as our most important gas. It supports the life of plants and animals. Pure oxygen is also used to treat patients with breathing difficulties, to support mountaineers and deep-sea divers and to treat polluted water.

Nitrogen is used in the food industry. Many foods are packed in an atmosphere of nitrogen because this stops the food 'going off'. When you open a bag of crisps, you may well be letting out nitrogen into the atmosphere. Because nitrogen does not burn it is also used to clean oil and road tankers. Grain silos are filled with nitrogen as a precaution against fire.

Carbon dioxide is used by plants to make sugars. We use the plants as our food and burn them for heat. It is used to make drinks fizzy and also as a fire extinguisher. Ice-cream sellers use solid carbon dioxide to keep their ice cream cold.

The noble gases are used in the lighting industry. Argon, krypton and xenon are used to fill light bulbs. Neon is used in illuminated coloured signs. Helium is a very light gas and so is used to fill balloons. It is also mixed with oxygen and used by deep-sea divers.

Activity pages

Does Air Weigh Anything?
Learning objectives
- To interpret results.
- To know that air has weight.

The weight of air is so little that it will be impossible for the children to calculate it. (1cm^3 of air normally weighs 0.0012g.) The larger the balloon, the easier it will be for children to interpret their findings.

The weight of 1cm^3 of air would be the difference in weight between the non-inflated balloon and the inflated balloon divided by the volume of air. (You could find the volume of air by immersing the inflated balloon in water and measuring in mls.)

Compressing Air
Learning objectives
- To know that air can be compressed.
- To know that compressed air can be used to lift heavy objects.

Air can be compressed because the molecules are far apart. There is a lot of space between its molecules. There is little space between the molecules in a liquid. They cannot be squashed together.

What is in the Air?
Learning objectives
- To know that air contains a mixture of gases including pollutants.
- To know that some of the pollutants can be controlled.

The children could suggest that pollution can be reduced by: use of alternative sources of electricity (e.g. wind, wave, solar power), use of public transport/bicycles/walking/electric vehicles, solar panels on houses, more woodland, smoke from factories being cleaned before emission.

Oral work

Discuss with the children the importance of air and why it is essential that the balance of the mixture is not changed.

Discuss what might happen if the climate were to become warmer.

Written work

The children could make a list of all the evidence they can think of to prove that air exists, for example it produces wind, it has weight, it holds water.

They could produce a poster aimed at informing other children about how they can reduce pollution.

ICT

Ask the children to find out about other gases that are present in the air that are detrimental to the environment. There is a lot of information available at the Environmental Agency web site (http://www.environment.agency.gov.uk).

Does Air Weigh Anything?

You will need

- Two balloons
- Balloon pump
- Piece of dowel
- Thread

 **Key Idea**   Air takes up space and has weight.

1. Tie a piece of thread to the centre of the piece of dowel. Tie the other end so that the dowel is free to move. Hang the balloons from the dowel so that it balances. Mark the dowel exactly where one of the balloons is and then remove the balloon. Inflate the balloon using a balloon pump. Now hang the balloon from the mark on the stick.

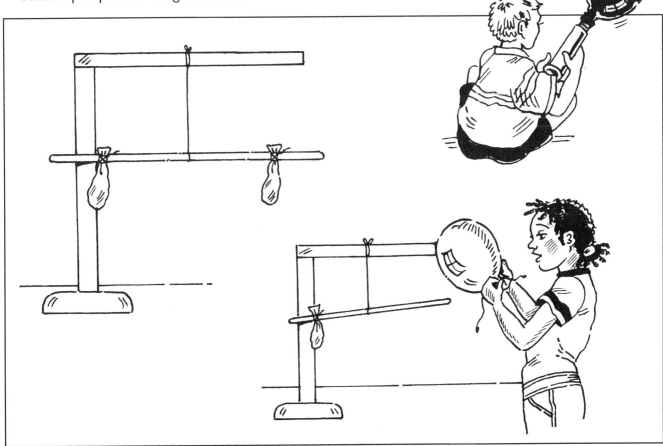

2. What do you notice?

_____

3. What does that tell you about air?

_____

4. Why do you think it is difficult to weigh air?

_____

 **NOW**   Imagine you had a weighing machine that was very accurate. How could you find the weight of 1cm³ of air? Write a list of instructions that your friend could use to weigh air.

Compressing Air

 **Key Idea** Air can be compressed. Compressed air can be used to lift heavy objects.

You will need
- Two plastic syringes
- Water
- Plastic tubing
- Polythene bags
- Strong thread
- Book
- Weights

1. Fill one syringe with water and the other with air. Put your finger on the end of the syringe filled with air and push the plunger. What do you notice?

2. Now put your finger on the end of the syringe filled with water and push the plunger. What do you notice?

3. What is the difference between air and water? Make a list of everyday examples of where air can be squeezed.

4. Attach two polythene bags together with plastic tubing as shown below. Make sure each of the bags has some air in it.

5. **a.** Put a book on one of the bags and squeeze the air from the other bag into it.
   b. What do you notice?
   c. What happens if you put more air into the bags before attaching them to the plastic tubing?
   d. What is the largest weight the bags can lift?
   e. When could air be used to lift weights?

 **NOW**   Find out how a pneumatic lift works. (For example, a car lift in a garage.)

What is in the Air?

Key Idea

Air is a mixture of nitrogen, oxygen, carbon dioxide, water vapour and other gases. We can help to reduce air pollution.

1. Read the following passage.

Air is a mixture of different gases. Most of the air is nitrogen, next is oxygen and then carbon dioxide. There is also a small amount of water vapour in the air. The amount changes as the weather changes. There are some other gases that are useful to us but come in tiny quantities and there are others that are very harmful to us.

The quality of the air we breathe affects our health and it may be responsible for changing the climate. In some parts of the world the quality of air is poor. This means that there are high levels of air pollution.

The main gas that is thought to be changing the climate is carbon dioxide. This is produced when fuels are burned. Some fuels are coal, oil, gas and wood. These are usually burned to produce electricity, fuel for transport, heat in the home and in industry. Many people think that we are producing too much carbon dioxide and that this is causing the Earth's atmosphere to become warmer. Some of the carbon dioxide is taken from the atmosphere by growing plants, particularly trees.

Vehicles can produce other harmful pollutants. Petrol and diesel vehicles produce over 75% of all carbon monoxide emitted in the UK. Carbon monoxide is a very poisonous gas. When a volcano erupts, gases are sent into the atmosphere. We cannot stop volcanoes but we can stop other ways of polluting.

2. Below is a picture of a polluting scene. Draw a ring around all those activities that are causing pollution and write an explanation of what is happening in each case.

3. What can industries and we do to reduce the pollution?

Changing State

The three states of matter are solid, liquid and gas. Every substance has its own melting and boiling point. Pure liquid freezes suddenly at a temperature called the freezing point. The freezing point of a liquid and the melting point of the solid are the same temperature. A pure liquid will boil at a definite temperature called the boiling point. (This occurs only at sea level – a kettle at the top of Snowdon will not boil at 100°C.) Mixtures melt over a range of temperatures, for example chocolate, whilst pure substances melt at one specific temperature (e.g. ice).

Some substances change immediately from a solid to a gas without going through the liquid state. This process is known as sublimation. Carbon dioxide sublimes from a solid to a gas.

In a solid the particles vibrate but are held in place by forces between other particles. As the solid is heated the particles vibrate faster until eventually they break apart and move around freely within the material. At this stage they are in liquid form. In order to break away from the other particles, energy must be put into the material.

Evaporation takes place over a range of temperatures. It occurs when individual particles or molecules obtain sufficient energy to break away from the rest of the liquid. The energy comes in the form of heat and will lead to a reduction in the temperature of the remaining liquid. If water is left on the skin to evaporate, then the skin feels cooler. Heat is taken from the body by the water molecules so that they can escape. A practical application of a liquid vapourising and so causing cooling is in the refrigerator. The gas is then made to condense (i.e. turn into a liquid). Heat is given out in the process.

When a liquid freezes, heat is given out. This can be felt in some heat pads – the liquid inside can be made to solidify and heat is given out in the process.

Activity pages

Evaporation
Learning objectives
- To know that an increase in temperature increases the rate of evaporation.
- To be able to plan an investigation.
- To be able to interpret findings.

Children could devise their own planning board or use the one provided.

Melting Points
Learning objectives
- To know that different substances melt at different temperatures.
- To make predictions and observe results.

Changes of State
Learning objectives
- To know the three states of matter.
- To know that the processes between the states of matter are reversible.

Discuss the fact that when some of the changes are reversed the substance looks the same, for example ice to water and back to ice again, while some will look different, for example margarine that has melted does not look the same when it becomes a solid again.

Answers to question 2 of activity sheet
a. evaporation, **b.** condensation, **c.** evaporation, **d.** freezing,
e. evaporation, **f.** melting, **g.** condensation, **h.** melting, **i.** melting.

Oral work

Ask the children to give examples of substances changing state. Can they think of examples other than water? For example, paint drying and chocolate, margarine or cheese melting.

Written work

Ask the children to imagine that they are a particle of water that is continuously heated and cooled. They could write a story or poem describing their experiences.

ICT

Children could repeat the activity of melting ice by taking the temperature using a data-logging device. They could repeat the activity in a warmer or a cooler environment, first predicting what the difference would be in the melting time. Children could research the melting and boiling points of common materials.

Evaporation

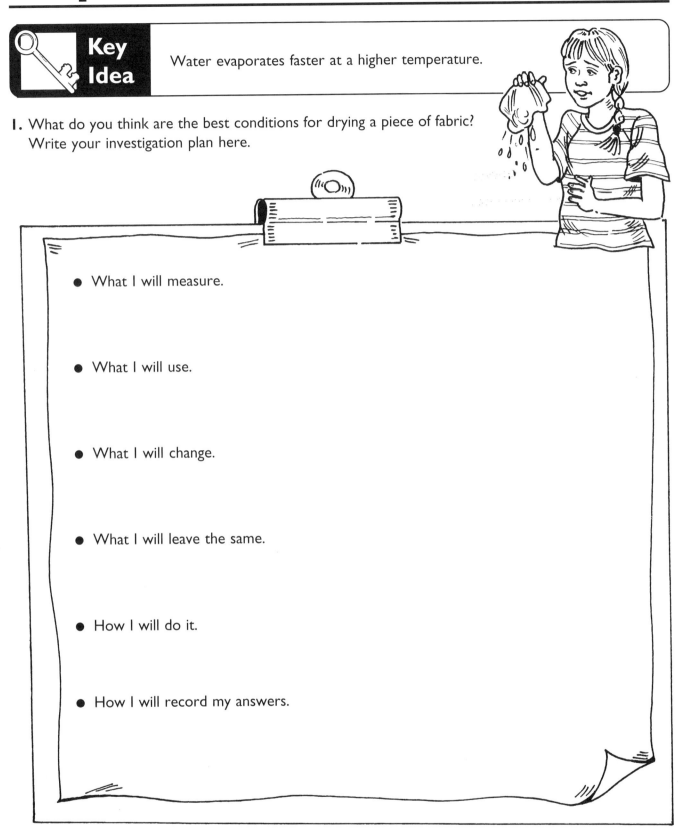

Key Idea

Water evaporates faster at a higher temperature.

1. What do you think are the best conditions for drying a piece of fabric? Write your investigation plan here.

- What I will measure.

- What I will use.

- What I will change.

- What I will leave the same.

- How I will do it.

- How I will record my answers.

2. Carry out the investigation.

3. Present your findings on one side of paper.

NOW Explain why water evaporates faster in some conditions than others.

Melting Points

Key Idea — Different substances melt at different temperatures. Mixtures of substances melt over a range of temperatures.

You will need
- Plate warmer or other warm surface e.g. radiator
- Metal dishes
- Margarine
- Ice
- Chocolate
- Candle wax
- Crayon wax
- Ice cream

- One way of finding whether a substance is pure is to watch it melt. If it melts at one temperature and changes immediately from solid to liquid then it is made of one material. If it melts over a range of temperatures then it is a mixture.

1. Collect the substances and predict the order in which they will melt. Order them from highest to lowest melting point in the table below.

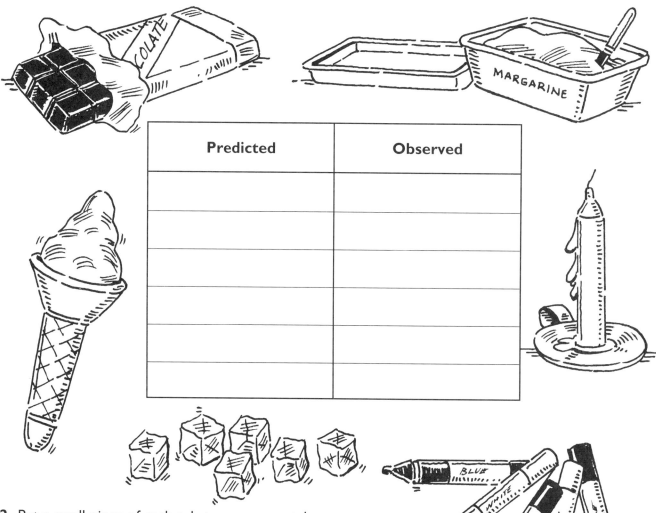

Predicted	Observed

2. Put a small piece of each substance on a metal dish and place the dish on a warm surface. Watch what happens to each of the substances.

3. Complete the table above by making a list of the order of melting. How close to your predicted order was your observed order?

NOW — Write down which of the substances are pure (i.e. they contain only one substance).

Changes of State

Matter can change from one state to another. The changes of state are: melting, freezing, evaporation, condensation and sublimation.

1. Write the names of the changes of state on the lines.

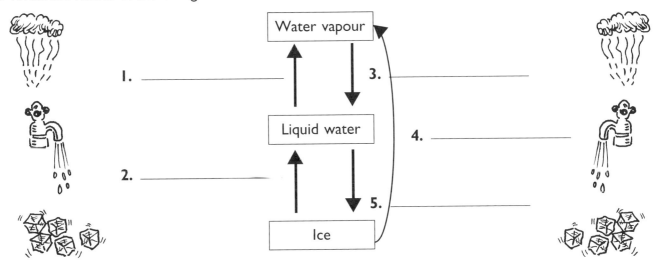

2. Give the scientific name for each of the following changes.

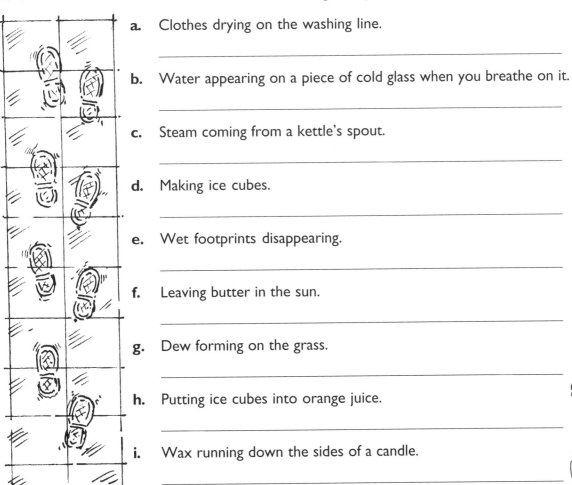

a. Clothes drying on the washing line.

_____

b. Water appearing on a piece of cold glass when you breathe on it.

_____

c. Steam coming from a kettle's spout.

_____

d. Making ice cubes.

_____

e. Wet footprints disappearing.

_____

f. Leaving butter in the sun.

_____

g. Dew forming on the grass.

_____

h. Putting ice cubes into orange juice.

_____

i. Wax running down the sides of a candle.

_____

 **NOW**   Make up three statements of your own.

The Story of Water

Background

Pure water freezes at 0°C and boils at 100°C at sea level. Many solids dissolve in water, even if only slightly. If a solid is dissolved in water it changes the way the water particles are held together. This causes the water to freeze at a lower temperature and to boil at a higher temperature.

When a liquid turns into a gas the particles need to gain enough heat energy to escape from the liquid. This can be felt when wet hands are left to dry. The hands become colder as the liquid water particles take heat from them before evaporating. Water vapour has more energy than liquid water at the same temperature. Similarly, when vapour changes back into a liquid it will release this extra heat energy.

When a substance melts, the particles need to gain heat energy so they can overcome the forces holding them together. If the liquid is then frozen, it will release this extra heat energy.

Activity pages

Boiling Water

Learning objectives
- To know that water boils at 100°C.
- To observe what happens when water is heated.

Safety – Ensure that the children are supervised during this activity.

Answers to activity sheet

2. Order	Observation	Explanation
2	Little bubbles rise to the top of the pan.	Tap water contains some dissolved air. The warmer the water, the less air can dissolve in the water. Air bubbles can be seen rising to the top of the pan when it is heated.
3	Large bubbles burst at the top of the water.	The bubbles are made of water vapour. They are lighter than the liquid water so rise to the surface.
5	The steam disappears.	The tiny water droplets evaporate in the air. Some of them may collect together to form water droplets on a cooler surface.
1	The inside of the top of the pan gets wet.	Water evaporates from the surface and condenses on the top of the pan. (This will only happen at the beginning otherwise the top of the pan will be warm and the vapour will not condense.)
4	Clouds of steam rise into the air.	The water vapour condenses in the air above the pan to form tiny droplets of water. This is known as steam.

3. Large bubbles rise to the top of the liquid.
4. The water evaporates and disappears into the air.

5. **A** between 20°C and 100°C, **B** 100°C, **C** 275 seconds.

Gritting the Roads

Learning objectives
- To understand that adding salt to ice lowers its freezing point.
- To hypothesise what happens when a solid melts.

Adding salt to ice lowers the melting point of the ice. The ice needs energy (as heat) so that the particles can break away from each other. The energy is obtained from the ice itself and so the temperature drops. Therefore the line where the temperature goes below 0°C is the ice plus salt.

Water Cycle

Learning objectives
- To know that water is sent to the air by evaporation, respiration and transpiration.
- To know that water returns as hail, rain or snow.

Answers to activity sheet
1. Evaporation of lakes/rivers/sea. Transpiration from plants.
3. The purple cloud should be the one over the mountain top.
4. The red area should be the lake, river and the sea.

Oral work

Discuss the facts that evaporation and condensation are reversible and that the Earth's supply of water is recycled. Children could discuss the value of water to people in various climates.

ICT

The children may be able to gather similar information to those given in the activities using datalogging equipment. They could research the rainfall of different areas of the world.

Boiling Water

Key Idea

Changes take place when water is heated.
Water boils at 100°C.

You will need
– Glass-sided pan
– Heat source

1. Half fill the pan with water and place it on the heat source. You will need an adult with you. Heat the pan of water and note all your observations. Try to explain what is happening at each stage by copying and completing the table below.

Observation	Explanation
Water appears on outside of the pan.	Water vapour condenses on to the cold surface.
Water disappears from the outside of the pan.	Water evaporates because the pan is warmer.

2. Here are some observations that another pupil recorded. Number them so that they are in the correct order.

Little bubbles rise to the top of the pan. ☐

The inside of the top of the pan gets wet. ☐

Large bubbles burst at the top of the water. ☐

Clouds of steam rise into the air. ☐

The steam disappears. ☐

3. How do you know when the water is boiling?

4. Where does the water go?

5. A temperature sensor was placed in a pan of water whilst it was heated. Here is the graph of the temperature changes. Mark on the graph:
   A – a point where the water was heating up
   B – the point where the water first started to boil
   C – the point where the heat was turned off.

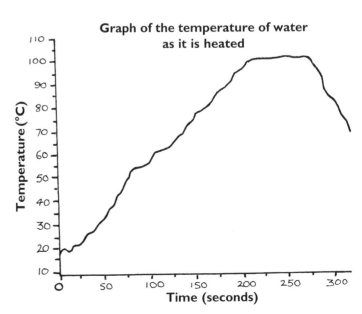

Graph of the temperature of water as it is heated

Temperature (°C) / Time (seconds)

Gritting the Roads

You will need
- Ice cubes
- Salt
- Two beakers
- Two thermometers
- Teaspoon
- Stopwatch

Key Idea	Pure water melts at 0°C. Impure water melts at a lower temperature.

● Road grit contains salt. This investigation should help you to see what happens when the roads are gritted in cold weather.

1. Place four ice cubes into each of the beakers. (It is better if the ice is crushed first.)
   Record the temperature of the ice.
   Put two teaspoonfuls of salt into one of the beakers.
   Record the temperature of the ice.

2. Observe what happens in each of the beakers. How long does it take for all the ice in each beaker to melt?

3. Why do you think the ice should be crushed?

4. What would happen if you put more salt on to the ice cubes?

5. a. How else could you get the ice to melt quickly?
   b. Could your method be used on the roads in winter? Explain your answer.

6. Here is a graph of the temperature changes that took place when one thermometer was placed in ice and another in ice that had some salt added to it.
   a. Write the word salt-ice against the line that had salt added to the ice. Explain your choice.
   b. Draw what you think the graph would have looked like if the room temperature had been 10° higher.

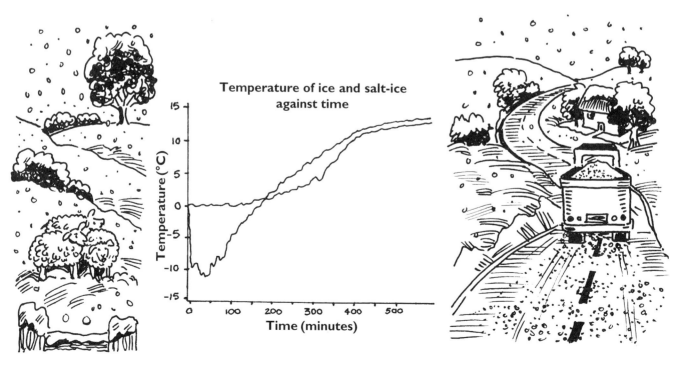

Temperature of ice and salt-ice against time

Temperature (°C) / Time (minutes)

Water Cycle

Key Idea

The water cycle never stops. Water evaporates into the atmosphere from oceans, rivers and lakes. Plants give out water vapour in transpiration. Animals give out water vapour through respiration. The water vapour condenses to form clouds. The water droplets grow until they fall as rain, snow etc.

1. Look at the diagram below and draw two more arrows to show where water vapour gets into the atmosphere.

2. Shade in the rainfall with a blue crayon.

3. Add arrows to the diagram to show the water cycle.

NOW

Pretend you are a water molecule. Send a postcard to your family about your travels. Remember the water cycle never stops.

The Earth and Sun

The Sun appears to move across the sky during the day, but it actually does not move around the Earth. The Earth, spinning on its own tilted axis as it orbits the Sun, in fact causes this apparent movement. The size of an object's shadow depends on the position of the Sun in the sky. When the Sun rises it is low in the sky and shadows are long. At midday the Sun appears highest in the sky and the shadows are shortest. After midday the Sun's location becomes more westerly and appears lower in the sky. The shadows then lengthen. The length of a shadow one hour after midday should be the same as one hour before midday. Before midday in the UK the shadows will be between West and North and after midday they will be between North and East. The Sun is in the direction opposite to the shadow.

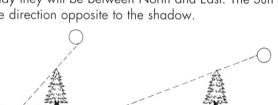

Between the tropics the shadow length can reduce to nothing at certain times of the year. This is due to the angle of tilt of the Earth. Between March and September, the North Pole faces towards the Sun whilst the South Pole faces away from the Sun. The converse is true between September and March. In the UK the shadows are shortest at midday on June 21st while the longest midday shadows occur on December 21st.

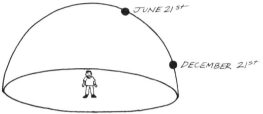

Day length changes throughout the year. The shortest day in the Northern Hemisphere is December 21st and the longest June 21st. The spring and autumn equinoxes are the days when there are 12 hours of day and 12 hours of night.

Changing Shadows

Learning objectives
- To understand that shadow size can change.
- To investigate shadow size.
- To interpret findings.

This activity is best carried out with a thin beam of light.

Shadow Length and Time

Learning objectives
- To know that the Sun rises in the East and sets in the West.
- To understand that the length and direction of a shadow can be used as an indication of the time.

Discuss how a sundial works – the position of the sun in the sky casts the shadow in a different direction, and the dial gives the time. Ask the children to devise a game where the length and direction of a shadow are given and a partner works out the time.

If the experiment on the activity sheet was done on the Equator, the shadow would reduce to nothing at midday.

Rise and Shine

Learning objectives
- To present data graphically.
- To find patterns.
- To interpret tabular and graphical data.

Ensure the children use appropriate vocabulary when discussing the movement of the Earth (e.g. revolve, spin, orbit, rotate, axis, sunrise, sunset).

Ask the children to imagine that they fell asleep for a very long time (a thousand years) before waking up. What evidence would they look for to find out which season of the year it was? They may suggest day length, shadow size and temperature.

The data for 'Shadow Length and Time' and for 'Rise and Shine' could be put into a spreadsheet and displayed graphically.

Changing Shadows

Key Idea

The length of a shadow depends on different factors including the distance of the light from the object, the distance of the surface on which the shadow is cast from the object and the angle at which the light meets the object.

You will need

– Darkened room
– Torch
– Pencil
– Plasticine to secure pencil

1. Working in a darkened room, shine the torch on to the pencil, keeping the torch about 30cm from the pencil, and observe where the shadow is. Make the length of the shadow as short as possible.

2. Explain why you think the shadow is so short. Draw a diagram in the box below to help you to explain.

_____

_____

_____

_____

3. Make the length of the shadow as long as possible.

4. Explain why you think the shadow is so long. Draw a diagram in the box below to help you to explain.

_____

_____

_____

_____

5. If a metre stick was placed upright and outside on a sunny day, how can the results of the activity you have just done relate to the length of the stick's shadow changing throughout the day?

_____

_____

_____

Shadow Length and Time

Key Idea — The length of a stick's shadow changes throughout the day.

1. Do this experiment in pairs at five regular intervals throughout the day. Hold the metre stick vertically in an open space and, record the length of its shadow and the direction of its shadow in the table below.

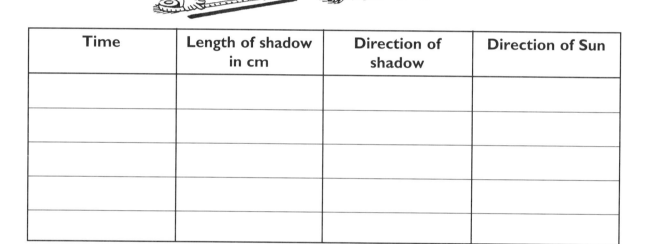

Time	Length of shadow in cm	Direction of shadow	Direction of Sun

2. Draw a graph of the length of shadow against time.

Length of shadow / Time

3. When is the shadow shortest?

4. When is the shadow longest?

5. What is the relationship between the length of the shadow and the direction of the Sun?

6. Explain why the length of the shadow changes during the day.

7. Draw a graph to show what you think would happen to the length of the shadow if you carried out this activity six months later in the year.

8. Draw a graph to show what you think would happen to the length of the shadow if you carried out this activity on the Equator.

Rise and Shine

Key Idea Times of sunrise and sunset change over the year. The amount of daylight across Britain is not the same on each day.

● The table below states approximate sunrise and sunset times for Glasgow and for London throughout the year. Calculate the day lengths and then plot graphs of day length against month for Glasgow and for London.

Date (1st)	Glasgow			London		
	Sunrise	Sunset	Day length	Sunrise	Sunset	Day length
January	0850	1550		0800	1600	
February	0800	1700		0730	1700	
March	0700	1800		0630	1800	
April	0645	2000		0630	1930	
May	0530	2100		0530	2030	
June	0430	2200		0500	2100	
July	0430	2210		0500	2100	
August	0530	2130		0530	2030	
September	0630	2100		0600	1940	
October	0730	1900		0700	1830	
November	0730	1630		0700	1630	
December	0830	1600		0750	1550	

● Use your graphs to answer the following questions.

1. What changes occur over a year in the time of sunrise in Glasgow?

2. How does this compare with the changes in sunrise in London?

3. What changes occur in the time of sunset throughout the year?

4. On which day do you think sunrise will be earliest?

5. On which day do you think sunset will be latest?

6. There is one month when the day length is the same in Glasgow and in London. Which month is it?

7. During which months does Glasgow have more daylight hours than London?

8. Explain why Glasgow has fewer daylight hours than London during the winter months.

Background

The Moon appears to change shape due to its rotation around the Earth and its changing position relative to the Sun. The continual changes in appearance are known as phases. The Moon does not emit light but is seen because it is lit up by the Sun – half its surface being bright and half being dark. The appearance of the Moon depends on the direction from which we view the bright hemisphere. Because the Moon is continually moving around the Earth this view changes each day.

The Moon takes 28 days to orbit the Earth; the direction of the orbit being the same as that of the Earth's rotation (i.e. towards the east). The Moon appears to rise in different directions and at different times throughout the lunar month.

When the Sun, Moon and Earth are in line, a new phase begins. At this stage the Moon is invisible from Earth because all the sunlight falling on the Moon is reflected away from the Earth. As the Moon orbits the Earth a crescent shape appears. This turns into a gibbous moon and then a full moon, at which point the Sun and the Moon are in opposite directions in the sky. As the Moon continues to orbit the Earth the same phases occur but in reverse order. The crescent of the new moon appears immediately after sunset whereas the opposite crescent of the old moon is visible just before sunrise. A nearly full moon usually appears early in the evening, towards the east, and can be seen nearly all night long.

Sometimes near to a new moon the entire face of the Moon is faintly visible. This is due to earthshine. This is the light reflected from the Earth onto the Moon, which is then reflected back to Earth.

Activity pages

Observing the Moon
Learning objectives
- To record observations.
- To identify patterns in observations.
- To know that the Moon's phases have a 28-day cycle.

The children are asked to observe the phases of the Moon over a month. It does not matter if the Moon is not visible every night. They will not be able to measure the direction of the Moon accurately but they may notice that its position changes throughout the night and the month.

Why Does the Moon Change Shape?
Learning objectives
- To simulate the changing shapes of the Moon.
- To interpret observations.

Phase Predictor
Learning objectives
- To use equipment to predict phases of the Moon.

The separate parts of the moon calculator should be stuck onto thin card.

Oral work

Children should discuss their observations and use the correct vocabulary: 'phase', 'new moon', 'crescent', 'gibbous', 'full'.

Written work

Children could research the solar system. They could write and produce a play that tries to convince others that the Earth is round. Research into the life of Galileo would help children to find out more about the history of science.

ICT

Children could use secondary sources, including videos and CD-ROM, to help them to understand how the Earth, Sun and Moon interact.

Observing the Moon

Key Idea

There is a pattern to the position, shape and rising of the Moon.

1. Observe the Moon over a 28-day period and draw in the shape of the Moon below.
Try to observe the Moon as soon as it appears in the sky.
Write the date on the first line.
Write the time of the appearance of the Moon on the second line.
Write the direction of the Moon on the third line.

2. Draw what you think the Moon will look like on the 29th day.

3. a. Find the drawing of the new moon (when the moon is not visible). Label it 1.
   b. Label the next moon 2 and so on.
   c. How many days after the new moon is the full moon?

29th day

4. What pattern do you notice about the time the Moon rises in the sky?

5. What pattern do you notice about the position of the Moon in the sky?

Why Does the Moon Change Shape?

Key Idea

The shape of the Moon is spherical with one bright hemisphere and one dark. The bright half of the Moon appears to change shape due to the direction of the Moon relative to the Sun.

You will need
- Darkened room
- Torch (with a narrow beam to avoid excessive stray light)
- Football
- Chair

When the Moon is changing from a new moon to a full moon we say it is 'waxing'.

When the Moon is changing from a full moon to an old moon we say it is 'waning'.

1. Working in threes, imagine the torch is the Sun, the football is the Moon and the chair is the Earth. Take it in turns to sit on the chair, to hold the torch and to hold the football. One person should stand some distance away and hold the torch so that it shines on the 'Moon'.
The person holding the 'Moon' should now walk around the 'Earth'. (Decide which way is north and walk anticlockwise around the 'Earth' from west to east.) The person on the chair needs to observe the light and dark areas of the 'Moon'.

2. Draw three shapes of light that can be made on the 'Moon' football.

3. Draw the positions of the 'Sun' and the 'Moon' when there is a full moon.

4. Draw the positions of the 'Sun' and the 'Moon' when there is a waning moon.

5. Draw the positions of the 'Sun' and the 'Moon' when there is a new moon.

6. Draw the positions of the 'Sun' and the 'Moon' when there is a waxing moon.

Phase Predictor

Key Idea

The phases of the Moon can be predicted.

You will need

- Scissors
- Thin card
- Split pin
- Ruler

● Find out what the Moon will be like today and on your next birthday using the following instrument.

● Cut out the three circles. Put circle 1 on top of circle 2 on top of circle 3 and attach them at the centre with a split pin.
Move circle 1 so that the arrow points to the correct month.
Move circle 2 so that the arrow points to the correct year.
Find the date on circle 1 (if the date is the 31st choose 1).
Now place a ruler or straight edge on the date so that it passes through the centre of the circle.
The number on the outside of the rim opposite your chosen date is the number of days since a new moon.

Circle 2

Circle 3

Circle 1

Making and Sending Sound

Background

Sound is heard when air in contact with the ear causes the eardrum to vibrate. Vibrations in air may be set up in a variety of ways, for example a tuning fork twanged; ruler or rubber band plucked; blowing inside a milk bottle. When a tuning fork is struck, the prongs move rapidly backwards and forwards. This causes the air around them to vibrate. When air vibrates the vibrations are propagated through the air as compression waves.

Sound can travel through materials other than air. It travels faster through a metal than through air because the particles in a metal are held closer together than in air. It is therefore easier to pass the vibrations through it. Sound can also travel through liquids, for example water. Sound cannot travel through a vacuum as there is nothing to vibrate.

Hard solids and springy materials can produce sounds. A balloon can be used to demonstrate vibrations in sound. The vibrations can be felt by touching it whilst whispering. The vibrations can be seen if rice grains are placed on a taut drum skin and the drum struck.

Some materials are better sound insulators than others. These materials absorb the sound energy whereas other materials might allow the sound to transmit through them or might reflect the sound. Sound insulators usually contain pockets of air or are soft (e.g. soft furnishings).

Our ears detect pressure changes in the air. These cause the eardrum to vibrate, which makes tiny bones in the middle ear vibrate. These vibrations are converted into electrical energy in the inner ear. This energy is transmitted to the brain where the brain makes sense of the 'message'. People who are subjected to continuous loud noise may damage their ears. Sometimes the bones in the middle ear become fixed and so cannot send the vibrations to the inner ear, or the cells in the inner ear are unable to convert the vibrations into electrical impulses. The damage can be permanent and can lead to deafness.

The loudness of sound is measured in decibels. Children should be encouraged to think about noises that may damage their ears so that they can take precautions if they are exposed to them.

Safety – Tell children it is unsafe to put objects into their ears.

Activity pages

Seeing Vibrations
Learning objectives
- To know that sounds are produced by vibrating objects.

Sometimes a vibrating object will not produce a sound because the speed of the vibrations is too slow (e.g. a pendulum). At other times the vibrations cannot be seen or felt because they are too fast.

Safety – Do not allow children to place the tuning fork against their teeth.

Sound Travels
Learning objectives
- To investigate materials that transmit sound.
- To plan an investigation.
- To know that sound travels through solids.

The children could put the block of wood on carpet, on plastic, on brick etc.

Safe and Sound
Learning objectives
- To know that very loud sounds can be damaging to the ears.
- To communicate information to others.

Oral work

Discuss where the children may be exposed to loud noises and what they might do to protect their hearing. The children could pretend they are deaf and try to communicate (other than by writing) to each other. This would highlight the difficulties some people face.

Written work

The children could produce a poster that informs others of the dangers of loud noises.

ICT

Sensing equipment can be used to find the loudness of noises. The quietest and loudest places in the school could be found.

Seeing Vibrations

Key Idea Sounds are made when objects or materials vibrate.

You will need
- Tuning fork
- Dish of water
- Drum
- Rice grains
- Inflated balloon

1. Strike a prong of the tuning fork on the tabletop and then touch the surface of the water with the prong. What happens?

2. Place six rice grains on the skin of a drum and then strike the drum gently. What happens?

3. Hold an inflated balloon against your lips and say and repeat your name. What happens?

4. What do the above three investigations show?

5. What other objects can you see or feel vibrating when they make a sound?

 **NOW**   Why do you think you cannot see or feel all objects vibrating when they make a sound?

Sound Travels

Key Idea — Sound travels through solids, liquids and gases.

You will need
- Block of wood
- Ruler
- Tape measure

1. Working in pairs, put a block of wood on your desk and get your partner to tap it gently with a ruler. Place your ear on the desk. What can you hear?

2. Move away from your partner so that you can only just not hear the sound. Measure the distance between you and your partner.

3. Place the block of wood on another hard surface and repeat the tapping and measuring. What do you notice?

4. **a.** Choose some other surfaces to place the block of wood against.
   b. Which materials allow the sound to travel most easily?
   c. Which materials do not let the sound travel well?

5. How would you carry out an investigation to find out if sound travels through water?

NOW — Try to explain why some materials allow sound to travel through them more easily than others.

Safe and Sound

Key Idea

Loud sounds can be harmful to the ear. It is sometimes necessary to reduce levels of sound.

- Loud noises can be dangerous. Noise is measured in units called decibels. The quietest sound that the ear can hear is the threshold of hearing. The older a person becomes the less well they hear. Some noises are so loud that they cause earache and headache. These sounds are above 120 decibels. Continuous loud noise may cause deafness. People who work in noisy places must wear ear protectors.

1. Look at the table below and think of another example for each noise.

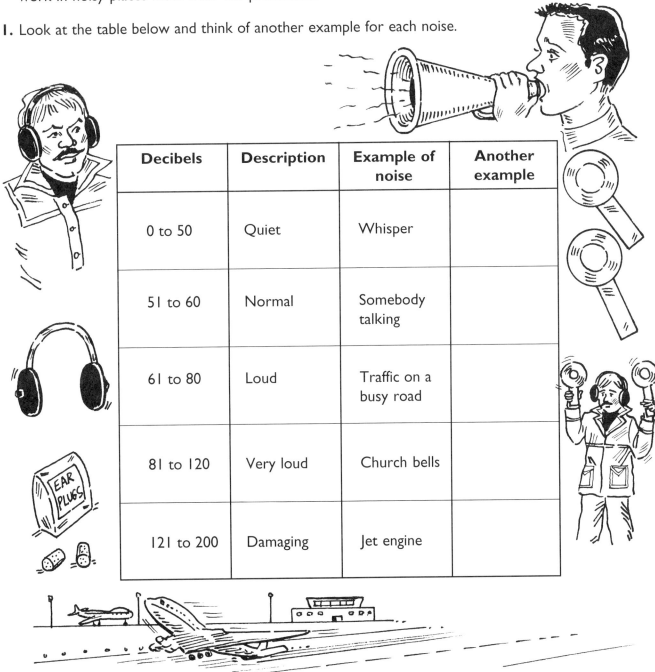

Decibels	Description	Example of noise	Another example
0 to 50	Quiet	Whisper	
51 to 60	Normal	Somebody talking	
61 to 80	Loud	Traffic on a busy road	
81 to 120	Very loud	Church bells	
121 to 200	Damaging	Jet engine	

2. List four groups of people who are at risk from noise pollution.

NOW

Make a poster that informs people who are at risk from noise pollution of what they should do to protect their ears.

Pitch and Loudness

The faster an object vibrates the higher the note it will produce. The speed of vibration is known as the frequency. Tuning forks will have a frequency stamped on to them. These can be used to show that the higher the frequency, the higher the note.

The frequency of a twanged piece of dowel can be altered by changing the length of the dowel that is vibrating – the longer the length, the lower the frequency and the lower the note. This is also true for string and wind instruments. In a wind instrument a column of air is made to vibrate – the longer the column, the lower the note.

The frequency also depends on the thickness of the material vibrating. The thicker the material, the lower the frequency at which it vibrates and the lower the note produced. Children should be shown different stringed instruments so that they can investigate the effect of

having thicker strings. If they are allowed to look inside a piano they will see different lengths and thicknesses of strings. The material of the strings also may change from copper to steel. Different materials produce different sounds.

Another way of raising the pitch is to increase the tension in the string.

The loudness of a note depends on the amount of energy it carries. If a string is plucked hard it will be given more energy. This energy will be transmitted to the surrounding air. This will cause the sound to be louder than if it had been plucked gently. The loudness may be increased by using a larger sound box.

Children should be encouraged to research instruments from around the globe, for example sitar, steel drum, guiro and stick, chajchas, conch, didgeridoo and lute, as well as the more traditional orchestral instruments.

Activity pages

Pitch
Learning objectives
- To investigate the relationship between frequency of vibration and pitch.
- To know that the longer the dowel or air column vibrating, the lower the pitch.

The children should be able to identify that the more straw there is in the water, the higher the pitch is and the longer the column of air the lower the pitch. When the children blow across the end of the straw they cause the air in it to vibrate. Wind instruments are constructed so that air can be made to vibrate.

Making Music
Learning objectives
- To investigate how loud sounds can be produced.
- To be able to design a musical instrument.

The Sound of Music
Learning objectives
- To understand that there are many different musical instruments.
- To identify instruments playing.

A good introduction to this activity is to play an extract from *Peter and the Wolf* by Prokofiev.

Oral work

The children could listen to music and identify the instruments being played. The children need to hear music that is not produced by electronic means if they are to develop an understanding of how sounds are produced and the range of musical instruments.

Written work

Ask the children to research instruments from around the world and display their findings. They might also collect examples of how animals produce sound, for example a rattle snake shakes rings of cartilage on the end of its tail, a cricket rubs its legs together, a humming bird flaps its wings and a bat uses echo location.

ICT

The children could research instruments and animal communication by using CD-ROMs. Sounds may be seen using pictures from an oscilloscope.

Pitch

Key Idea   Pitch is the highness or lowness of the sound. This is related to the frequency of vibrations.

1. Place one end of the dowel on your tabletop and hold it with your hand. Twang the other end of the dowel and observe what happens. Move the dowel so that there is less overhang. Twang it again.

2. a. What happens to the speed of the vibrations?

    b. What happens to the pitch of the sound produced?

    c. What is the link between the speed of the vibrations and the pitch of the note?

    d. What is the relationship between the length of the dowel that vibrates and the pitch of the note?

3. Predict what will happen if you blow across the top of a straw when the bottom is placed in water.

4. Half fill a beaker with water. Put a straw in it and blow across the top. What happens?

5. Move the straw slowly up and down in the water as you blow across the top. What happens to the sound? Why do you think this is?

Making Music

 **Key Idea** | Stringed instruments can be tuned by changing the length, thickness and tension of the strings.

You will need
- Different-sized rubber bands
- Selection of boxes

1. Make a musical instrument by placing three different-sized rubber bands around one of your boxes.

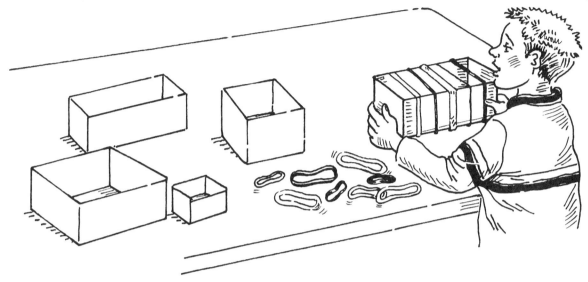

2. What do you think will happen if you twang each of the rubber bands in turn?

_____

3. Test your hypothesis to see if you were correct.

_____

4. How many ways can you find to make the sounds louder?

_____

5. Use other rubber bands to produce a scale.

6. Make a tune with your instrument.

7. Write down your tune so that others can play it.

 **NOW** | Design some other musical instruments that could be made using household items.

The Sound of Music

You will need
- Books about instruments
- Pictures of a variety of musical instruments
- Music CDs

Key Idea

Changing the speed of vibration of materials can create music.

1. Find two instruments that are plucked. _____

   _____

2. Find two instruments that are struck. _____

   _____

3. Find two instruments that are blown. _____

   _____

4. Find two instruments that are bowed. _____

   _____

5. Complete the following table.

Name of instrument	How is it played?	What vibrates?	How is the pitch altered?

NOW Listen to a piece of music and make a list of the instruments that you think are producing the music. If you do not know the name of the instrument then draw what you think it looks like.

Glossary

Alveoli (p4) Tiny air sacs in the lungs.

Balanced diet (p8) Healthy diet that consists of foods from each of the four main food groups – **proteins, carbohydrates, vitamins** and **minerals,** and **fats.**

Breathing rate (pp4–5) Rate at which a person breathes. One full breath means to inhale and exhale. Breathing rate increases with exercise.

Capillaries (p4) Small blood vessels linking arteries and veins

Carbohydrate (pp8, 10–11) Material in food that the body uses for energy. A **balanced diet** needs to contain carbohydrates (for example in bread, pasta, rice, cereal and potatoes).

Carbon monoxide (pp4, 20, 23) Pollutant that is colourless, odourless and tasteless, but extremely dangerous. It can be found in tobacco smoke, petrol fumes and in emissions from industry, transport and homes.

Circulatory system (pp4, 6) System that transports blood around the body, consisting of arteries, veins and the heart.

Compression waves (p40) Vibration that is in the same direction as the transfer of energy.

Eardrum (p40) Membrane that separates the outer ear from the **middle ear.** Sound waves strike the eardrum, causing it to vibrate.

Equator (p34) Imaginary line around the centre of the Earth.

Evaporation (pp24–25, 27–29, 31) Turning from liquid to gas, for example when water dries.

Fat (pp8–11) Material in food that the body uses for stored energy. A **balanced diet** needs to contain fats (for example in milk, cheese, butter and yoghurt), but too much fat can lead to serious health problems, such as obesity and heart disease.

Fertilisation (pp12–13) In plants, this is the result of the pollen and the egg in the ovary joining together.

Fibre (pp8, 10) Material in food that the body uses to keep it healthy. Fibre is not digested by the body, but a **balanced diet** needs to contain fibre (for example in wholemeal bread, cereal and baked beans).

Frequency (pp44–45) Number of vibrations repeated in a unit of time.

Germination (pp12, 15) When a plant begins to grow; when a plant sprouts.

Gestation period (pp16, 19) Period in the womb between conception and birth.

Kilojoules (pp8, 11) Measure of the energy value of food.

Life cycle (12–13, 16, 18) Development of a plant or animal that consists of stages between the beginning of life and death.

Metamorphosis (p16) Change in form.

Middle ear (p40) The middle ear is separated from the outer ear by the **eardrum.** The middle ear contains three small bones. When the **eardrum** vibrates the waves pass through the small bones to the inner ear, which sets in motion fluid. This agitates a membrane that stimulates thousands of sensory hairs that in turn stimulate the auditory nerve to send messages to the brain.

Mineral (pp8, 11) Material found in food that the body uses to make strong bones and teeth, to help blood clot and for various other bodily functions. A **balanced diet** needs to contain minerals (for example from fruit and vegetables).

Molecule (pp20, 31) Small particle of a material/substance.

Nutrient (p11) Substance that is essential to provide nourishment for life.

Photosynthesis (p12) Process in which green plants use the energy of sunlight to make food. Carbon dioxide from the air and water from the soil are combined with chlorophyll by using energy from sunlight to produce glucose sugar.

Pitch (pp44–45, 47) Describes whether a sound is high or low.

Pollination (pp12–13) When the pollen from a flower is transferred to the stigma of another plant.

Pollutant (pp20, 23, 43) Something that pollutes (contaminates) that which is clean.

Processed food (p10) Food that has undergone several manufacturing stages.

Protein (pp8, 10–11) Material in food that the body uses to build new cells. A **balanced diet** needs to contain proteins (for example from lentils, beans, meat, eggs and fish).

Pulse (pp4–5) Beat caused by blood that rushes out of the heart into the arteries. This rush of blood sets up a wave or pulse that travels along the arteries. When you feel your pulse, you feel each wave as it passes along an artery.

Respiration (pp8, 28, 31) Act of breathing. To take in air, change the gases in it and pass out the changed air.

Respiratory system (p4) System of the passage of air through inhalation and exhalation (i.e. the nose, mouth trachea, lungs).

Seed dispersal (pp12, 14) Seeds are dispersed from their source in a number of ways. They may be carried by wind or animals. Animals may eat and excrete the seed, or it may stick to an animal's body and dropped away from the plant.

Sublimation (pp24, 27) Changing from a solid to a gas without going through the liquid state.

Transpiration (pp28, 31) In plants, this is the loss of water by evaporation through the pores (stomata) of the leaves and through the plant's surface cells.

Tropics (p32) Region between the Tropic of Cancer and the Tropic of Capricorn – the imaginary lines north and south of the Equator.